Mike was good, but he did one thing
that his Mom and Dad didn't like.
Mike never just said things.
He yelled them!

Mike yelled when he went out.
"So long Mom! So long Dad!
I'm out of here!"

Or he yelled when he came in.
"I'm back, Mom! How's it
going, Dad?"

Mike yelled when things were not going well.
"Mom! Dad! Look at my bike! I have a flat!
Can you help me fix it?"

Mike even yelled when things were fine.
"Mom! Dad! This looks great!
When do we eat?"

"How can we get Mike to stop
yelling all the time?" said Dad.
"There has to be a way," said Mom.
Then she yelled, "Look!"

Mike's mother and father saw
a snake, asleep in their house!
"How did it get in here?" said Dad.
"Sh-sh-sh, it's sleeping," said Mom.
"Never wake a sleeping snake."

FIDO

Then Mike came in and saw the snake.
"How did a snake get in here?" he yelled.
"Sh-sh-sh, it's sleeping," said Mom.
"Never wake a sleeping snake."

The snake was there for some time,
asleep in the house.
Mike never yelled — not even one time!
He thought, "Never wake a sleeping snake."

Before long some people came to get the snake.
Even they didn't wake it up!
But after that, Mike never yelled.
(Well, not much anyway.)